FRIENDSHIP
with
GOD
WORKBOOK

D1571609

JAMIE MOORE

DOXAZO

Friendship with God: Discussion Guide and 40-Day Journal

Copyright © 2021 by Jamie Moore

Doxazo Press

Scripture quotations, unless otherwise indicated, are from the ESV® Bible (The Holy Bible, English Standard Version®), copyright © 2001 by Crossway. 2011 Text Edition. Used by permission. All rights reserved.

Scripture references marked NIV are taken from The Holy Bible, New International Version®, NIV®. Copyright © 1973, 1978, 1984 by Biblica, Inc.™ Used by permission. All rights reserved worldwide.

Scripture quotations marked NRSV are from the New Revised Standard Version Bible, copyright © 1989 National Council of the Churches of Christ in the United States of America. Used by permission. All rights reserved worldwide.

ISBN: 978-1-7362926-3-1

Typesetting by InkSmith Editorial Services

Free Resources for Readers
The *Friendship with God*
Video Course
(Over 2 hours of video content from Jamie)

The *Friendship with God* video course is designed to enhance this discussion guide and help you practically apply the principles of this book in your daily life.

The video course is available for individual or group use. You can get free access to the video course at:

https://www.jamiemoore.org/friendshipfreebies

To Abba

You roared over me.

I will roar for you—forever!

Contents

Introduction: The Friendship with God Framework 1

Discussion Guide 3

    Chapter One: Presence Lost 4

    Chapter Two: God with Us 6

    Chapter Three: Seeking His Presence 8

    Chapter Four: Show Me Your Glory 10

    Chapter Five: The Hiding Place 12

    Chapter Six: Home Is Where the Spirit Is 14

    Chapter Seven: Reading God's Word Relationally 16

    Chapter Eight: Prayer and Hearing God's Voice 18

    Chapter Nine: His Voice Shapes You 20

    Chapter Ten: Commissioned in His Presence 22

    Chapter Eleven: Living "Doubly" Present 24

    Chapter Twelve: Community of Presence 26

40-Day Journal 31

About The Author 113

INTRODUCTION: THE FRIENDSHIP WITH GOD FRAMEWORK

Time + Conversation + Activity = Friendship with God

These are the three ingredients for you to become a friend of God: time, conversation, and activity—together with Him as your friend.

You can be a friend of God *today*. Will you intentionally seek Him?

This book is designed as a companion resource to *Friendship with God*. To get the most out of this resource:

1. Gather a group to go through the discussion guide together. Remember, Jesus is uniquely among us when we gather in His name. (Matthew 18:20)
2. Download the free video resource and use it in conjunction with the discussion guide
3. Commit as a group to take the 40-Day Journal challenge together
4. Keep in touch with me! I want to hear what God is doing in your group and be an encouragement to you in any way that I can. Email me here: jamie@jamiemoore.org

Friendship with God is available to you *today*.

The Father is pursuing you *today*.

Jesus loves you and wants to talk with you *today*.

The Holy Spirit wants to move through you *today*.

Friend, I encourage you to take off the shame coverings and come out of hiding. Practice the relational presence of God, and receive His peace in every circumstance of your life. Talk to Jesus and allow His words to shape you with His identity over your life. Join the Holy Spirit on the adventure of what He has planned to accomplish through you today.

You will join a long line of God's friends who walked with Him and pleased Him. Walk in friendship with God today.

Much love to you,

Jamie

DISCUSSION GUIDE

You will have as little [of God] as you are satisfied with. . . . The [person] who is content to follow Christ afar off will never know the radiant wonder of His nearness. The [one] who is willing to settle for a joyless, barren life will never experience the joy of the Holy Spirit or the deep satisfaction of fruitful living . . . .

You now have as much [of God] as you really want. Every [person] is as close to God as he wants to be; he is as holy and as full of the Spirit as he wills to be.

– A. W. Tozer

Chapter One

PRESENCE LOST

And they heard the sound of the LORD God walking in the garden in the cool of the day, and the man and his wife hid themselves from the presence of the LORD God among the trees of the garden.

– Genesis 3:8

QUESTIONS TO DISCUSS:

1. Consider the "Friendship Framework" (Friendship = Time + Conversation + Activity) and reflect on some of your closest friendships. Which "ingredient" is the most difficult for you in those friendships? Which is the most natural for you in those relationships?

_____

_____

_____

_____

_____

_____

2. Do you consider yourself a "friend of God?" Why or why not?

_____

_____

_____

_____

_____

_____

3. Describe the four steps in the enemy's scheme. Use examples in your own life.

_____

_____

_____

_____

_____

_____

4. Read Genesis 3:1-24. What are the primary "fig leaves" that you fashion to cover up yourself from God and others? How have you tried to "fix" these things in the past?

_____

_____

_____

_____

_____

_____

RECOMMENDED READING FOR DEEPER STUDY:

Tozer, A. W. *The Knowledge of the Holy: The Attributes of God.* New York: Harper & Row, 1961.

Packer, J. I. *Concise Theology: A Guide to Historic Christian Beliefs.* Wheaton, IL: Tyndale House, 1993.

Chapter Two

GOD WITH US

I will make my dwelling among you, and my soul shall not abhor you. And I will walk among you and will be your God, and you shall be my people.

– Leviticus 26:11–12

My dwelling place shall be with them, and I will be their God, and they shall be my people.

– Ezekiel 37:27

Behold, the dwelling place of God is with man. He will dwell with them, and they will be his people, and God himself will be with them as their God.

– Revelation 21:3

QUESTIONS TO DISCUSS:

1. Have you found yourself disoriented when you read the Bible? What strategies or resources have you used to re-orient yourself?

_____

_____

_____

_____

_____

2. Describe the three-part covenant goal of God found in Scripture from Genesis to Revelation and reflect on the truth: *God wants to be with you.*

_____

_____

_____

_____

_____

3. Have you experienced forgiveness of your sin by faith in Jesus? Have you turned to Him as your substitute who died in your place on the cross? Have you received His forgiveness? If so, describe when this happened. If not, why not?

_____

_____

_____

_____

_____

_____

4. In what part of the biblical story are we actively living in right now? What are we supposed to be doing? What does God want to do through us as His portable temples?

_____

_____

_____

_____

_____

_____

RECOMMENDED READING FOR DEEPER STUDY:

Duvall, J. Scott, and J. Daniel Hays. *God's Relational Presence: The Cohesive Center of Biblical Theology*. Grand Rapids, MI: Baker Academic: A Division of Baker Publishing Group, 2019.

Wright, Christopher J. H. *Salvation Belongs to Our God: Celebrating the Bible's Central Story*. Edited by David Smith and Joe M. Kapolyo. Global Christian Library Series. Cumbria, UK: Langham Global Library, 2013.

Chapter Three

SEEKING HIS PRESENCE

You will seek me and find me, when you seek me with all your heart.

– Jeremiah 29:13

QUESTIONS TO DISCUSS:

1. Since the Hebrew word for "presence" means "face" – how does that affect your understanding of the command to "seek God's presence?" What does it mean to seek His presence?

_____

_____

_____

_____

_____

_____

2. How would your life look different, if you obsessively pursued the presence of God every day? Consider the Psalmist's words: "seek His presence continually." (Psalm 105:4)

_____

_____

_____

_____

_____

_____

3. Reflect on the idea of holy selfishness in your Christian walk. What does C.S. Lewis mean when he says we are "far too easily pleased."

_____

_____

_____

_____

_____

_____

4. Read Luke 15:11-32. How does the story of the prodigal son inform your view of God, the Father?

_____

_____

_____

_____

_____

_____

RECOMMENDED READING FOR DEEPER STUDY:

Tozer, A. W. *The Pursuit of God*. Camp Hill, PA: WingSpread, 2006.

Keller, Timothy. *The Prodigal God: Recovering the Heart of the Christian Faith*. 1st ed. New York: Dutton, 2008.

Chapter Four

SHOW ME YOUR GLORY

If your presence will not go with me, do not bring us up from here. . . .
Please show me your glory.

– Exodus 33:15,18

QUESTIONS TO DISCUSS:

1. How have you disqualified yourself from having a face-to-face friendship with God, just like Moses?

_____

_____

_____

_____

_____

_____

2. Reflect on A. W. Tozer's words: "You have as much of God as you actually want." What does he mean when he says this? How is this similar or different to Moses' cry: "Show me your glory?" (Exodus 33:18)

_____

_____

_____

_____

_____

_____

3. Read Exodus 40:36-38. This is a summary statement of how the people of Israel followed the glory and presence of God. What would your life look like if you followed the glory and presence of God each day like the Israelites?

_____

_____

_____

_____

_____

_____

4. How will you practically practice the presence of God this week?

_____

_____

_____

_____

_____

_____

RECOMMENDED READING FOR DEEPER STUDY:

Blackaby, Henry. *Experiencing God.* Nashville, TN: Broadman & Holman, 1994.

Brother Lawrence. *The Practice of the Presence of God.* New Kensington, PA: Whitaker House, 1982.

Chapter Five

THE HIDING PLACE

God is our refuge and strength, a very present help in trouble. Therefore we will not fear.

– Psalm 46:1–2

QUESTIONS TO DISCUSS:

1. What is the thing in your life that makes you the most anxious?

_____

_____

_____

_____

_____

_____

2. Read and reflect on Psalm 46. What does the Psalmist say about God and His nature in this passage?

_____

_____

_____

_____

_____

_____

3. In this chapter of the book, the author writes that, "Peace is a person . . . Jesus is peace . . . Jesus is not stressed or worried about anything. He is completely at peace." What does it mean to live "present-tense with Jesus" rather than "future-tense without Jesus?"

_____

_____

_____

_____

_____

4. Review the practical steps at the end of this chapter. Take a few moments to practice step 3: "Give your anxiety to Jesus, and receive His peace." Spend some time in prayer, casting your anxiety on Jesus, because He cares for you. Give Him your worry and receive His peace.

_____

_____

_____

_____

_____

RECOMMENDED READING FOR DEEPER STUDY:

Anderson, Neil. _The Bondage Breaker_. Eugene, OR: Harvest House Publishers, 1993.

Tozer, A. W. _That Incredible Christian: How Heaven's Children Live on Earth_. Camp Hill, PA: WingSpread, 1964.

Chapter Six

HOME IS WHERE THE SPIRIT IS

Jesus answered him, "If anyone loves me, he will keep my word, and my Father will love him, and we will come to him and make our home with him."

– John 14:23

QUESTIONS TO DISCUSS:

1. Do you believe that God wants to dwell and be "at home" with you? Why or why not?

_____

_____

_____

_____

_____

_____

2. Describe in your own words the five things that Jesus teaches about the Holy Spirit in John 14.

_____

_____

_____

_____

_____

_____

3. Reflect on 2 Corinthians 3:18 and the theological process of Sanctification. What is your job and what is the Holy Spirit's job in this process?

_____

_____

_____

_____

_____

_____

4. Review the practical steps at the end of this chapter. Take a few moments to practice step 1: "Be continually filled with the Holy Spirit." This is an ongoing command from Scripture, to be filled by God with His Spirit, over and over again. Spend some time in prayer and ask the Father to fill you with His Spirit. (Luke 11:13)

_____

_____

_____

_____

_____

_____

RECOMMENDED READING FOR DEEPER STUDY:

Fee, Gordon D. *God's Empowering Presence: The Holy Spirit in the Letters of Paul.* Grand Rapids, MI: Baker Academic, 2011.

Keener, Craig S. *Gift & Giver: The Holy Spirit for Today.* Grand Rapids, MI: Baker Academic, 2001.

Chapter Seven

READING GOD'S WORD RELATIONALLY

You search the Scriptures because you think that in them you have eternal life; and it is they that bear witness about me, yet you refuse to come to me that you may have life.

– John 5:39–40

QUESTIONS TO DISCUSS:

1. How do you view the Bible? Compare and contrast these two approaches to Bible reading: academic reading and relational reading.

_____

_____

_____

_____

_____

_____

2. Reflect on Jesus' interaction with the religious scholars of His day in John 5:39-40. What delusion does this passage expose? How is this danger present for us today?

_____

_____

_____

_____

_____

_____

3. What is the delusion found in James 1:22? Why is this danger so difficult for us to avoid? What practices have you put into place to avoid this delusion?

_____

_____

_____

_____

_____

_____

4. Review the practical steps at the end of this chapter. Discuss the role of the Holy Spirit in your Bible reading. How are you planning on putting these practical steps into practice?

_____

_____

_____

_____

_____

_____

RECOMMENDED READING FOR DEEPER STUDY:

Tozer, A. W. *God's Pursuit of Man.* Camp Hill, PA: WingSpread, 2007.

Keener, Craig S. *Spirit Hermeneutics: Reading Scripture in Light of Pentecost.* Grand Rapids, MI: William B. Eerdmans Publishing Company, 2016.

Chapter Eight

PRAYER AND HEARING GOD'S VOICE

My sheep hear my voice, and I know them, and they follow me.

– John 10:27

QUESTIONS TO DISCUSS:

1. Describe a time when you felt you heard the Good Shepherd speak clearly to you? What did He say? What happened?

   _____

   _____

   _____

   _____

   _____

   _____

2. Do you find prayer and other spiritual disciplines easy or difficult? Why?

   _____

   _____

   _____

   _____

   _____

   _____

3. Reflect on Psalm 23 and John 10:1-30. What steps do you need to take to experience a daily rhythm with Jesus as your Good Shepherd? How will this look different than a "quiet time" in the morning?

_____

_____

_____

_____

_____

_____

4. Review the 10 practical steps at the end of this chapter. Take some time and go through all 10 steps. Share with your community what you believe you heard from the Good Shepherd.

_____

_____

_____

_____

_____

_____

RECOMMENDED READING FOR DEEPER STUDY:

Deere, Jack S. *Surprised by the Voice of God: How God Speaks Today through Prophecies, Dreams, and Visions.* Grand Rapids, MI: Zondervan Academic, 2010.

Foster, Richard J. *Celebration of Discipline: The Path to Spiritual Growth.* New York: HarperCollins Publishers, 1998.

Chapter Nine

HIS VOICE SHAPES YOU

You are my beloved Son; with you I am well pleased.

– Luke 3:22

Fear not, for I have redeemed you; I have called you by name, you are mine. ... You are precious in my eyes, and honored, and I love you.

– Isaiah 43:1,4

QUESTIONS TO DISCUSS:

1. Which voices and influences in your life have shaped your identity the most?

   _____

   _____

   _____

   _____

   _____

   _____

2. Consider the concept of the imposter and fig leaves. What imposter identity have you embraced during your life?

   _____

   _____

   _____

   _____

   _____

   _____

3. Reflect on 2 Corinthians 5:21 and the text to "Be Not Afraid" by Craig Courtney. (You can even listen to the author's youth choir sing this song on YouTube.) What does it mean to receive your primary identity from the Father, in Christ?

_____

_____

_____

_____

_____

_____

4. Review the practical steps at the end of this chapter. Discuss the importance of collecting identity statements and Gospel scriptures for personal use and memorization. How are you planning on putting these practical steps into practice?

_____

_____

_____

_____

_____

_____

RECOMMENDED READING FOR DEEPER STUDY:

Manning, Brennan. *Abba's Child: The Cry of the Heart for Intimate Belonging*. Colorado Springs, CO: NavPress, 2009.

Virgo, Terry. *God's Lavish Grace*. Grand Rapids, MI: Monarch Books, 2004.

Chapter Ten

COMMISSIONED IN HIS PRESENCE

As the Father has sent me, so I am sending you.

– John 20:21

QUESTIONS TO DISCUSS:

1. Abraham, Gideon, Isaiah, and the disciples all had reasons to believe that God wouldn't (or couldn't) use them. Which of these similar beliefs have kept you from embracing the adventure of walking in God's purpose for your life? (Too old? Too scared? Too sinful? Too inexperienced?) Are there other limiting beliefs that hold you back?

_____

_____

_____

_____

_____

_____

2. Describe the four-part commissioning pattern discussed in this chapter and consider, specifically, the identity change of Abraham, Gideon, Isaiah, and the disciples. How did these individuals receive their new identities?

_____

_____

_____

_____

_____

_____

3. Read Ephesians 2:8-10 and reflect on the author's statement: "Before God created anything, He had you in mind and planned things for you to do and accomplish by His power. Before He spoke a single galaxy into being, the Father had specific assignments for you to walk in today."

_____

_____

_____

_____

_____

_____

4. Review the practical steps at the end of this chapter. Consider committing with a group of other believers to practice these steps for 40 days.

_____

_____

_____

_____

_____

_____

RECOMMENDED READING FOR DEEPER STUDY:

Mueller, George. *Autobiography of George Mueller: A Million and a Half in Answer to Prayer.* London: J. Nisbet and Co., 1914.

Pullinger, Jackie. *Chasing the Dragon.* Ventura, CA: Regal Books, 2007.

Chapter Eleven

LIVING "DOUBLY" PRESENT

I am the vine; you are the branches. Whoever abides in me and I in him, he
it is that bears much fruit, for apart from me you can do nothing.

– John 15:5

QUESTIONS TO DISCUSS:

1. What did you think about the story of Jesus healing the sushi waitress in
   Cincinnati? Do you think He would ever use you to do the same thing?
   Why or why not?

   _____

   _____

   _____

   _____

   _____

   _____

2. Explain how Jesus was "doubly present" in his ministry. What does that
   mean? Other than with the woman at the well, can you think of another
   encounter where Jesus modeled this ministry rhythm?

   _____

   _____

   _____

   _____

   _____

   _____

3. Reflect on John 15:1-17 and compare with John 14:12-14 and John 16:23-24. What do these passages teach us about God's nature? What is promised in these passages? What should we do, based on what Jesus said in these passages?

    _____

    _____

    _____

    _____

    _____

    _____

4. Review the practical steps at the end of this chapter. Take a few moments to practice speaking or serving in the power of the Holy Spirit. Spend time praying for one another in your group.

    _____

    _____

    _____

    _____

    _____

    _____

RECOMMENDED READING FOR DEEPER STUDY:

Deere, Jack S. *Why I Am Still Surprised by the Power of the Spirit: Discovering How God Speaks and Heals Today.* Grand Rapids, MI: Zondervan, 2020.

Storms, Sam. *Practicing the Power: Welcoming the Gifts of the Holy Spirit in Your Life.* Grand Rapids, MI: Zondervan, 2017.

Wimber, John, and Kevin Springer. *Power Evangelism.* Ventura, CA: Regal, 2009.

Chapter Twelve

COMMUNITY OF PRESENCE

For where two or three are gathered in my name, there am I among them.
– Matthew 18:20

QUESTIONS TO DISCUSS:

1. Describe a time when you had a meal that was very uncomfortable. What made you feel the way you did? Describe the best meal experience you ever had. Why do you think it was such a good experience?

_____

_____

_____

_____

_____

_____

2. Read Jesus' first miracle in John 2:1-11. Compare this with the fact that the Pharisees called Jesus a "friend of sinners." (Luke 7:34) What does this tell us about God? What is the Father like, based on the behavior of Jesus?

_____

_____

_____

_____

_____

_____

3. Reflect on your experience in community with others. Is it difficult for you to be vulnerable and in community with others in the Body of Christ? Why or why not?

_____

_____

_____

_____

_____

_____

4. Review the practical steps at the end of this chapter. Consider planning regularly scheduled meals together with your community to continue discussing friendship with God and how you can live out Acts 2:42-47.

_____

_____

_____

_____

_____

_____

RECOMMENDED READING FOR DEEPER STUDY:

Frost, Michael. *Surprise the World: The Five Habits of Highly Missional People*. Colorado Springs, CO: NavPress, 2016.

Whitney, Donald. *Family Worship*. Wheaton, IL: Crossway, 2016

12 GOSPEL SCRIPTURES FOR LIFE

In Chapter Nine of *Friendship with God*, I shared my story of struggling to believe that I am who God says I am. The enemy whispers in my ear, especially after I've sinned against God, and tempts me to stop believing the Gospel.

I've learned that if I memorize Gospel Scriptures, then I can use them in warfare against the enemy's lies. The following is my personal list of Gospel Scriptures that I have memorized and use regularly to combat the enemy and his schemes against me.

Friend, when you mess up and sin, remind yourself of these gospel truths. Tell that voice to go to literal hell, and then run back into the arms of the Father. Receive forgiveness. You *will* mess up. When you do, don't wait. Go to the Father by faith in Jesus. Restored identity is found in the arms of the Father.

Mark 10:45, "For even the Son of Man came not to be served but to serve, and to give his life as a ransom for many."

John 3:16-17, "For God so loved the world, that he gave his only Son, that whoever believes in him should not perish but have eternal life. For God did not send his Son into the world to condemn the world, but in order that the world might be saved through him."

Romans 5:8, "God shows his love for us in that while we were still sinners, Christ died for us."

Romans 8:1, "There is therefore now no condemnation for those who are in Christ Jesus."

Romans 10:9-10, "If you confess with your mouth that Jesus is Lord and believe in your heart that God raised him from the dead, you will be saved. For with the heart one believes and is justified, and with the mouth one confesses and is saved."

1 Corinthians 15:3-4, "For I delivered to you as of first importance what I also received: that Christ died for our sins in accordance with the Scriptures, that he was buried, and that he was raised on the third day."

2 Corinthians 5:21, "For our sake he made him to be sin who knew no sin, so that in him we might become the righteousness of God."

Galatians 2:20, "I have been crucified with Christ. It is no longer I who live, but Christ who lives in me. And the life I now live in the flesh I live by faith in the Son of God, who loved me and gave himself for me."

1 Peter 2:24-25, "He himself bore our sins in his body on the tree, that we might die to sin and live to righteousness. By his wounds you have been healed. For you were straying like sheep, but have now returned to the Shepherd and Overseer of your souls."

1 John 1:9, "If we confess our sins, he is faithful and just to forgive us our sins and to cleanse us from all unrighteousness."

1 John 4:10, "In this is love, not that we have loved God but that he loved us and sent his Son to be the propitiation for our sins."

Revelation 5:9-10, "And they sang a new song, saying, "Worthy are you to take the scroll and to open its seals, for you were slain, and by your blood you ransomed people for God from every tribe and language and people and nation, and you have made them a kingdom and priests to our God, and they shall reign on the earth."

40-DAY JOURNAL

You have as much of God as you want. So, commit to grow in friendship with Him. Take the next forty days to establish a new rhythm of presence, conversation, and adventure with Jesus.

Every day, show up to be with Him. When you get up in the morning, say to Jesus, "Here I am. Speak, Lord. Send me!" Put the practical steps from each chapter into practice for the next forty days. Develop new habits, and watch how your life will be changed by the presence, voice, and power of God in your life.

For forty days, schedule time to be with God. Get into the Bible and read it, relationally. Listen to Jesus speak over you and shape your identity. Share what you are hearing and learning from the Holy Spirit with one other person for forty days.

This journal is designed to help you practice this new rhythm of walking in friendship with God. This resource provides forty Scriptures for you to reflect on with space to journal your reflections and what you are hearing from God as you listen. Each day, you will read a Scripture, be still, and listen to what Jesus may say to you.

Don't forget to gather a group and do this 40-Day challenge together! It will provide accountability and a perfect place to share what you are learning and hearing from God.

> I ought to pray before seeing any one. Often when I sleep long, or meet with others early, and then have family prayer, and breakfast, and forenoon callers, often it is eleven or twelve o'clock before I begin secret prayer. . .
>
> Family prayer loses much of its power and sweetness; and I can do no good to those who come to seek from me. The conscience feels guilty, the soul unfed, the lamp not trimmed. Then, when secret prayer comes, the soul is often out of tune.
>
> I feel it is far better to begin with God—to see his face first—to get my soul near Him before it is near another.
>
> **– Robert Murray McCheyne**

I Have Called You Friends

Verse of the Day

You are my friends if you do what I command you. No longer do I call you servants, for the servant does not know what his master is doing; but I have called you friends, for all that I have heard from my Father I have made known to you. You did not choose me, but I chose you and appointed you that you should go and bear fruit and that your fruit should abide, so that whatever you ask the Father in my name, he may give it to you.

– John 15:14-16

Reflection

_____

_____

_____

_____

_____

_____

_____

_____

_____

_____

_____

_____

_____

_____

_____

WHERE ARE YOU?

Verse of the Day

But the serpent said to the woman, "You will not surely die. For God knows that when you eat of it your eyes will be opened, and you will be like God, knowing good and evil." So when [Eve] saw that the tree was good for food, and that it was a delight to the eyes, and that the tree was to be desired to make one wise, she took of its fruit and ate, and she also gave some to [Adam] who was with her, and he ate. Then the eyes of both were opened, and they knew that they were naked. And they sewed fig leaves together and made themselves loincloths.

And they heard the sound of the Lord God walking in the garden in the cool of the day, and the man and his wife hid themselves from the presence of the Lord God among the trees of the garden. But the Lord God called to the man and said to him, "Where are you?" And he said, "I heard the sound of you in the garden, and I was afraid, because I was naked, and I hid myself."

. . . And the Lord God made for Adam and for his wife garments of skins and clothed them.

– Genesis 3:4-9, 21

REFLECTION

_____

_____

_____

_____

_____

_____

_____

_____

_____

Day 3

I WILL MAKE MY DWELLING WITH YOU

Verses of the Day

I will make my dwelling among you, and my soul shall not abhor you. And I will walk among you and will be your God, and you shall be my people.

– Leviticus 26:11–12

My dwelling place shall be with them, and I will be their God, and they shall be my people.

– Ezekiel 37:27

Behold, the dwelling place of God is with man. He will dwell with them, and they will be his people, and God himself will be with them as their God. He shall wipe away every tear from their eyes, and death shall be no more, neither shall there be mourning, nor crying, nor pain anymore, for the former things have passed away.

– Revelation 21:3-4

REFLECTION

_____

_____

_____

_____

_____

_____

_____

_____

You Will Seek Me and Find Me

Verse of the Day

For I know the plans I have for you, declares the Lord, plans for welfare and not for evil, to give you a future and a hope. Then you will call upon me and come and pray to me, and I will hear you. You will seek me and find me, when you seek me with all your heart.

– Jeremiah 29:11-13

REFLECTION

_____

_____

_____

_____

_____

_____

_____

_____

_____

_____

_____

_____

_____

_____

_____

_____

_____

SEEK HIS PRESENCE CONTINUALLY

Verse of the Day

Oh give thanks to the Lord; call upon his name; make known his deeds among the peoples! Sing to him, sing praises to him; tell of all his wondrous works! Glory in his holy name; let the hearts of those who seek the Lord rejoice! Seek the Lord and his strength; seek his presence continually!

– Psalm 105:1-4

REFLECTION

_____

_____

_____

_____

_____

_____

_____

_____

_____

_____

_____

_____

_____

_____

_____

I THIRST FOR YOU, GOD

Verses of the Day

As a deer pants for flowing streams, so pants my soul for you, O God. My soul thirsts for God, for the living God.

– Psalm 42:1–2

O God, you are my God; earnestly I seek you; my soul thirsts for you; my flesh faints for you, as in a dry and weary land where there is no water.

– Psalm 63:1

I stretch out my hands to you; my soul thirsts for you like a parched land.

– Psalm 143:6

REFLECTION

_____

_____

_____

_____

_____

_____

_____

_____

_____

_____

_____

_____

_____

_____

FULLNESS OF JOY

Verse of the Day

I say to the Lord, "You are my Lord; I have no good apart from you. . . . I have set the Lord always before me; because he is at my right hand, I shall not be shaken. Therefore my heart is glad, and my whole being rejoices; my flesh also dwells secure. For you will not abandon my soul to Sheol, or let your holy one see corruption. You make known to me the path of life; in your presence there is fullness of joy; at your right hand are pleasures forevermore.

– Psalm 16:2, 8-11

REFLECTION

_____

_____

_____

_____

_____

_____

_____

_____

_____

_____

_____

_____

_____

_____

HERE I AM

Verse of the Day

Now Moses was keeping the flock of his father-in-law, Jethro, the priest of Midian, and he led his flock to the west side of the wilderness and came to Horeb, the mountain of God.

And the angel of the LORD appeared to him in a flame of fire out of the midst of a bush. He looked, and behold, the bush was burning, yet it was not consumed. And Moses said, "I will turn aside to see this great sight, why the bush is not burned."

When the LORD saw that he turned aside to see, God called to him out of the bush, "Moses, Moses!" And he said, "Here I am."

Then he said, "Do not come near; take your sandals off your feet, for the place on which you are standing is holy ground."

– Exodus 3:1–5

REFLECTION

_____

_____

_____

_____

_____

_____

_____

_____

_____

_____

Day 9

FACE TO FACE

Verse of the Day

Now Moses used to take the tent and pitch it outside the camp, far off from the camp, and he called it the tent of meeting. And everyone who sought the Lord would go out to the tent of meeting, which was outside the camp. Whenever Moses went out to the tent, all the people would rise up, and each would stand at his tent door, and watch Moses until he had gone into the tent. When Moses entered the tent, the pillar of cloud would descend and stand at the entrance of the tent, and the Lord would speak with Moses. And when all the people saw the pillar of cloud standing at the entrance of the tent, all the people would rise up and worship, each at his tent door. Thus the Lord used to speak to Moses face to face, as a man speaks to his friend. When Moses turned again into the camp, his assistant Joshua the son of Nun, a young man, would not depart from the tent.

– Exodus 33:7-11

REFLECTION

_____

_____

_____

_____

_____

_____

_____

_____

_____

_____

_____

_____

SHOW ME YOUR GLORY

Verse of the Day

Moses said to the Lord, "You have been telling me, 'Lead these people,' but you have not let me know whom you will send with me. You have said, 'I know you by name and you have found favor with me.' If you are pleased with me, teach me your ways so I may know you and continue to find favor with you. Remember that this nation is your people.

The Lord replied, "My Presence will go with you, and I will give you rest." Then Moses said to him, "If your Presence does not go with us, do not send us up from here. How will anyone know that you are pleased with me and with your people unless you go with us? What else will distinguish me and your people from all the other people on the face of the earth?" And the Lord said to Moses, "I will do the very thing you have asked, because I am pleased with you and I know you by name.

Then Moses said, "Now show me your glory."

– Exodus 33:12-18 (NIV)

REFLECTION

_____

_____

_____

_____

_____

_____

_____

_____

_____

_____

_____

Day 11

FOLLOW HIS GLORY AND PRESENCE

Verse of the Day

Then the cloud covered the tent of meeting, and the glory of the Lord filled the tabernacle. And Moses was not able to enter the tent of meeting because the cloud settled on it, and the glory of the Lord filled the tabernacle. Throughout all their journeys, whenever the cloud was taken up from over the tabernacle, the people of Israel would set out. But if the cloud was not taken up, then they did not set out till the day that it was taken up. For the cloud of the Lord was on the tabernacle by day, and fire was in it by night, in the sight of all the house of Israel throughout all their journeys.

– Exodus 40:34-38

REFLECTION

_____
_____
_____
_____
_____
_____
_____
_____
_____
_____
_____
_____
_____
_____

MY HIDING PLACE

Verses of the Day

He who dwells in the shelter of the Most High will abide in the shadow of the Almighty. I will say to the LORD, "My refuge and my fortress, my God, in whom I trust."

– Psalm 91:1–2

You are a hiding place for me; you preserve me from trouble; you surround me with shouts of deliverance.

– Psalm 32:7

In the cover of your presence you hide them from the plots of men; you store them in your shelter from the strife of tongues.

– Psalm 31:20

You are my hiding place and my shield.

– Psalm 119:114

God is our refuge and strength, a very present help in trouble. Therefore we will not fear.

– Psalm 46:1–2

REFLECTION

_____

_____

_____

_____

_____

_____

_____

_____

Strengthened Himself in the Lord

Verses of the Day

And when David and his men came to the city, they found it burned with fire, and their wives and sons and daughters taken captive. Then David and the people who were with him raised their voices and wept until they had no more strength to weep. . . . And David was greatly distressed, for the people spoke of stoning him, because all the people were bitter in soul, each for his sons and daughters. But David strengthened himself in the Lord his God.

– 1 Samuel 30:3-4, 6

I love you, O Lord, my strength. The Lord is my rock and my fortress and my deliverer, my God, my rock, in whom I take refuge, my shield, and the horn of my salvation, my stronghold. I call upon the Lord, who is worthy to be praised, and I am saved from my enemies.

– Psalm 18:1-3

Reflection

_____

_____

_____

_____

_____

_____

_____

_____

_____

_____

PEACE! BE STILL!

Verse of the Day

On that day, when evening had come, [Jesus] said to them, "Let us go across to the other side." And leaving the crowd, they took him with them in the boat, just as he was. And other boats were with him. And a great windstorm arose, and the waves were breaking into the boat, so that the boat was already filling.

But he was in the stern, asleep on the cushion. And they woke him and said to him, "Teacher, do you not care that we are perishing?" And he awoke and rebuked the wind and said to the sea, "Peace! Be still!" And the wind ceased, and there was a great calm. He said to them, "Why are you so afraid? Have you still no faith?" And they were filled with great fear and said to one another, "Who then is this, that even the wind and the sea obey him?"

– Mark 4:35-41

REFLECTION

_____

_____

_____

_____

_____

_____

_____

_____

_____

_____

_____

_____

MY PEACE I GIVE TO YOU

Verse of the Day

Peace I leave with you; my peace I give to you. Not as the world gives do I give to you. Let not your hearts be troubled, neither let them be afraid.

– John 14:27

"I have said these things to you, that in me you may have peace. In the world you will have tribulation. But take heart; I have overcome the world."

– John 16:33

REFLECTION

_____

_____

_____

_____

_____

_____

_____

_____

_____

_____

_____

_____

_____

_____

Do Not Be Anxious About Anything

Verse of the Day

Rejoice in the Lord always; again I will say, rejoice. Let your reasonableness be known to everyone. The Lord is at hand; do not be anxious about anything, but in everything by prayer and supplication with thanksgiving let your requests be made known to God. And the peace of God, which surpasses all understanding, will guard your hearts and your minds in Christ Jesus.

Finally, brothers, whatever is true, whatever is honorable, whatever is just, whatever is pure, whatever is lovely, whatever is commendable, if there is any excellence, if there is anything worthy of praise, think about these things. What you have learned and received and heard and seen in me—practice these things, and the God of peace will be with you.

– Philippians 4:4-9

Reflection

_____

_____

_____

_____

_____

_____

_____

_____

_____

_____

_____

HOME IS WHERE THE SPIRIT IS

Verse of the Day

And I will ask the Father, and he will give you another Helper, to be with you forever, even the Spirit of truth, whom the world cannot receive, because it neither sees him nor knows him. You know [the Holy Spirit], for he dwells with you and will be in you. "I will not leave you as orphans; I will come to you. . . If anyone loves me, he will keep my word, and my Father will love him, and we will come to him and make our home with him. Whoever does not love me does not keep my words. And the word that you hear is not mine but the Father's who sent me. "These things I have spoken to you while I am still with you. But the Helper, the Holy Spirit, whom the Father will send in my name, he will teach you all things and bring to your remembrance all that I have said to you.

– John 14:16-18, 23-26

REFLECTION

_____

_____

_____

_____

_____

_____

_____

_____

_____

_____

_____

_____

SPIRIT OF ADOPTION

Verse of the Day

But when the fullness of time had come, God sent forth his Son, born of woman, born under the law, to redeem those who were under the law, so that we might receive adoption as sons. And because you are sons, God has sent the Spirit of his Son into our hearts, crying, "Abba! Father!" So you are no longer a slave, but a son, and if a son, then an heir through God.

– Galatians 4:4-7

For all who are led by the Spirit of God are sons of God. For you did not receive the spirit of slavery to fall back into fear, but you have received the Spirit of adoption as sons, by whom we cry, "Abba! Father!" The Spirit himself bears witness with our spirit that we are children of God, and if children, then heirs—heirs of God and fellow heirs with Christ.

– Romans 8:14-17

REFLECTION

_____

_____

_____

_____

_____

_____

_____

_____

_____

_____

_____

_____

ONE DEGREE OF GLORY TO ANOTHER

Verse of the Day

Now the Lord is the Spirit, and where the Spirit of the Lord is, there is freedom. And we all, with unveiled face, beholding the glory of the Lord, are being transformed into the same image from one degree of glory to another. For this comes from the Lord who is the Spirit.

– 2 Corinthians 3:17-18

REFLECTION

_____

_____

_____

_____

_____

_____

_____

_____

_____

_____

_____

_____

_____

_____

_____

BE FILLED WITH THE HOLY SPIRIT

Verses of the Day

Look carefully then how you walk, not as unwise but as wise, making the best use of the time, because the days are evil. Therefore do not be foolish, but understand what the will of the Lord is. And do not get drunk with wine, for that is debauchery, but be filled with the Spirit.

– Ephesians 5:15-18

On the last day of the feast, the great day, Jesus stood up and cried out, "If anyone thirsts, let him come to me and drink. Whoever believes in me, as the Scripture has said, 'Out of his heart will flow rivers of living water.'" Now this he said about the Spirit, whom those who believed in him were to receive, for as yet the Spirit had not been given, because Jesus was not yet glorified.

– John 7:37-39

And I tell you, ask, and it will be given to you; seek, and you will find; knock, and it will be opened to you. For everyone who asks receives, and the one who seeks finds, and to the one who knocks it will be opened. What father among you, if his son asks for a fish, will instead of a fish give him a serpent; or if he asks for an egg, will give him a scorpion? If you then, who are evil, know how to give good gifts to your children, how much more will the heavenly Father give the Holy Spirit to those who ask him!

– Luke 11:9-13

REFLECTION

_____

_____

_____

_____

_____

_____

_____

Day 21

SPEAK, LORD

Verse of the Day

Now the boy Samuel was ministering to the Lord in the presence of Eli. And the word of the Lord was rare in those days; there was no frequent vision. At that time Eli, whose eyesight had begun to grow dim so that he could not see, was lying down in his own place. The lamp of God had not yet gone out, and Samuel was lying down in the temple of the Lord, where the ark of God was. Then the Lord called Samuel, and he said, "Here I am!" and ran to Eli and said, "Here I am, for you called me." But he said, "I did not call; lie down again." So he went and lay down. And the Lord called again, "Samuel!" and Samuel arose and went to Eli and said, "Here I am, for you called me." But he said, "I did not call, my son; lie down again." Now Samuel did not yet know the Lord, and the word of the Lord had not yet been revealed to him. And the Lord called Samuel again the third time. And he arose and went to Eli and said, "Here I am, for you called me." Then Eli perceived that the Lord was calling the boy. Therefore Eli said to Samuel, "Go, lie down, and if he calls you, you shall say, 'Speak, Lord, for your servant hears.' " So Samuel went and lay down in his place. And the Lord came and stood, calling as at other times, "Samuel! Samuel!" And Samuel said, "Speak, for your servant hears."

– 1 Samuel 3:1-10

REFLECTION

_____

_____

_____

_____

_____

_____

_____

_____

You Search the Scriptures

Verses of the Day

[Jesus said] You search the Scriptures because you think that in them you have eternal life; and it is they that bear witness about me, yet you refuse to come to me that you may have life.

– John 5:39-47

And this is eternal life, that they know you, the only true God, and Jesus Christ whom you have sent.

– John 17:3

Reflection

_____

_____

_____

_____

_____

_____

_____

_____

_____

_____

_____

_____

_____

_____

Day 23

BURNING HEARTS

Verse of the Day

That very day two of them were going to a village named Emmaus, about seven miles from Jerusalem, and they were talking with each other about all these things that had happened. While they were talking and discussing together, Jesus himself drew near and went with them. But their eyes were kept from recognizing him. And he said to them, "What is this conversation that you are holding with each other as you walk?" And they stood still, looking sad. Then one of them, named Cleopas, answered him, "Are you the only visitor to Jerusalem who does not know the things that have happened there in these days?" And he said to them, "What things?" And they said to him, "Concerning Jesus of Nazareth, a man who was a prophet mighty in deed and word before God and all the people, and how our chief priests and rulers delivered him up to be condemned to death, and crucified him. But we had hoped that he was the one to redeem Israel. Yes, and besides all this, it is now the third day since these things happened. Moreover, some women of our company amazed us. They were at the tomb early in the morning, and when they did not find his body, they came back saying that they had even seen a vision of angels, who said that he was alive. Some of those who were with us went to the tomb and found it just as the women had said, but him they did not see." And he said to them, "O foolish ones, and slow of heart to believe all that the prophets have spoken! Was it not necessary that the Christ should suffer these things and enter into his glory?" And beginning with Moses and all the Prophets, he interpreted to them in all the Scriptures the things concerning himself. So they drew near to the village to which they were going. He acted as if he were going farther, but they urged him strongly, saying, "Stay with us, for it is toward evening and the day is now far spent." So he went in to stay with them. When he was at table with them, he took the bread and blessed and broke it and gave it to them. And their eyes were opened, and they recognized him. And he vanished from their sight. They said to each other, "Did not our hearts burn within us while he talked to us on the road, while he opened to us the Scriptures?

– Luke 24:13-32

REFLECTION

_____

_____

DOERS OF THE WORD

Verse of the Day

But be doers of the word, and not hearers only, deceiving yourselves. For if anyone is a hearer of the word and not a doer, he is like a man who looks intently at his natural face in a mirror. For he looks at himself and goes away and at once forgets what he was like. But the one who looks into the perfect law, the law of liberty, and perseveres, being no hearer who forgets but a doer who acts, he will be blessed in his doing.

– James 1:22-25

REFLECTION

_____

_____

_____

_____

_____

_____

_____

_____

_____

_____

_____

_____

_____

_____

_____

_____

THE LORD IS MY SHEPHERD

Verse of the Day

The Lord is my shepherd; I shall not want. He makes me lie down in green pastures. He leads me beside still waters. He restores my soul. He leads me in paths of righteousness for his name's sake. Even though I walk through the valley of the shadow of death, I will fear no evil, for you are with me; your rod and your staff, they comfort me. You prepare a table before me in the presence of my enemies; you anoint my head with oil; my cup overflows. Surely goodness and mercy shall follow me all the days of my life, and I shall dwell in the house of the Lord forever.

– Psalm 23:1-6

REFLECTION

_____

_____

_____

_____

_____

_____

_____

_____

_____

_____

_____

_____

_____

_____

Day 26

I AM THE GOOD SHEPHERD

Verses of the Day

The thief comes only to steal and kill and destroy. I came that they may have life and have it abundantly. I am the good shepherd. The good shepherd lays down his life for the sheep. He who is a hired hand and not a shepherd, who does not own the sheep, sees the wolf coming and leaves the sheep and flees, and the wolf snatches them and scatters them. He flees because he is a hired hand and cares nothing for the sheep. I am the good shepherd. I know my own and my own know me, just as the Father knows me and I know the Father; and I lay down my life for the sheep. And I have other sheep that are not of this fold. I must bring them also, and they will listen to my voice. So there will be one flock, one shepherd. For this reason the Father loves me, because I lay down my life that I may take it up again. No one takes it from me, but I lay it down of my own accord. I have authority to lay it down, and I have authority to take it up again. This charge I have received from my Father.

– John 10:10-18

Surely he has borne our griefs and carried our sorrows; yet we esteemed him stricken, smitten by God, and afflicted. But he was pierced for our transgressions; he was crushed for our iniquities; upon him was the chastisement that brought us peace, and with his wounds we are healed. All we like sheep have gone astray; we have turned—every one—to his own way; and the Lord has laid on him the iniquity of us all.

– Isaiah 53:4-6

REFLECTION

_____

_____

_____

_____

_____

_____

MY SHEEP HEAR MY VOICE

Verse of the Day

My sheep hear my voice, and I know them, and they follow me. I give them eternal life, and they will never perish, and no one will snatch them out of my hand. My Father, who has given them to me, is greater than all, and no one is able to snatch them out of the Father's hand. I and the Father are one.

– John 10:27-30

REFLECTION

_____

_____

_____

_____

_____

_____

_____

_____

_____

_____

_____

_____

_____

_____

_____

_____

LISTEN TO HIM!

Verses of the Day

Now as they went on their way, Jesus entered a village. And a woman named Martha welcomed him into her house. And she had a sister called Mary, who sat at the Lord's feet and listened to his teaching. But Martha was distracted with much serving. And she went up to him and said, "Lord, do you not care that my sister has left me to serve alone? Tell her then to help me." But the Lord answered her, "Martha, Martha, you are anxious and troubled about many things, but one thing is necessary. Mary has chosen the good portion, which will not be taken away from her."

– Luke 10:38-42

And after six days Jesus took with him Peter and James and John, and led them up a high mountain by themselves. And he was transfigured before them, and his clothes became radiant, intensely white, as no one on earth could bleach them. And there appeared to them Elijah with Moses, and they were talking with Jesus. And Peter said to Jesus, "Rabbi, it is good that we are here. Let us make three tents, one for you and one for Moses and one for Elijah." For he did not know what to say, for they were terrified. And a cloud overshadowed them, and a voice came out of the cloud, "This is my beloved Son; listen to him." And suddenly, looking around, they no longer saw anyone with them but Jesus only.

– Mark 9:2-8

REFLECTION

_____

_____

_____

_____

_____

_____

_____

AS THE FATHER HAS SENT ME, SO I AM SENDING YOU

Verse of the Day

On the evening of that day, the first day of the week, the doors being locked where the disciples were for fear of the Jews, Jesus came and stood among them and said to them, "Peace be with you." When he had said this, he showed them his hands and his side. Then the disciples were glad when they saw the Lord. Jesus said to them again, "Peace be with you. As the Father has sent me, even so I am sending you." And when he had said this, he breathed on them and said to them, "Receive the Holy Spirit.

– John 20:19-22

REFLECTION

_____

_____

_____

_____

_____

_____

_____

_____

_____

_____

_____

_____

_____

HERE I AM, SEND ME

Verse of the Day

In the year that King Uzziah died I saw the Lord sitting upon a throne, high and lifted up; and the train of his robe filled the temple. Above him stood the seraphim. Each had six wings: with two he covered his face, and with two he covered his feet, and with two he flew. And one called to another and said: "Holy, holy, holy is the Lord of hosts; the whole earth is full of his glory!" And the foundations of the thresholds shook at the voice of him who called, and the house was filled with smoke. And I said: "Woe is me! For I am lost; for I am a man of unclean lips, and I dwell in the midst of a people of unclean lips; for my eyes have seen the King, the Lord of hosts!" Then one of the seraphim flew to me, having in his hand a burning coal that he had taken with tongs from the altar. And he touched my mouth and said: "Behold, this has touched your lips; your guilt is taken away, and your sin atoned for." And I heard the voice of the Lord saying, "Whom shall I send, and who will go for us?" Then I said, "Here I am! Send me."

– Isaiah 6:1-8

REFLECTION

_____

_____

_____

_____

_____

_____

_____

_____

_____

_____

THEY HAD BEEN WITH JESUS

Verse of the Day

And as [Peter and John] were speaking to the people, the priests and the captain of the temple and the Sadducees came upon them, greatly annoyed because they were teaching the people and proclaiming in Jesus the resurrection from the dead. And they arrested them and put them in custody until the next day, for it was already evening. But many of those who had heard the word believed, and the number of the men came to about five thousand. On the next day their rulers and elders and scribes gathered together in Jerusalem, with Annas the high priest and Caiaphas and John and Alexander, and all who were of the high-priestly family. And when they had set them in the midst, they inquired, "By what power or by what name did you do this?"

Then Peter, filled with the Holy Spirit, said to them, "Rulers of the people and elders, if we are being examined today concerning a good deed done to a crippled man, by what means this man has been healed, let it be known to all of you and to all the people of Israel that by the name of Jesus Christ of Nazareth, whom you crucified, whom God raised from the dead—by him this man is standing before you well. This Jesus is the stone that was rejected by you, the builders, which has become the cornerstone. And there is salvation in no one else, for there is no other name under heaven given among men by which we must be saved." Now when they saw the boldness of Peter and John, and perceived that they were uneducated, common men, they were astonished. And they recognized that they had been with Jesus.

– Acts 4:1-13

REFLECTION

_____

_____

_____

_____

_____

_____

WE ARE HIS WORKMANSHIP

Verse of the Day

For by grace you have been saved through faith. And this is not your own doing; it is the gift of God, not a result of works, so that no one may boast. For we are his workmanship, created in Christ Jesus for good works, which God prepared beforehand, that we should walk in them.

– Ephesians 2:8-10

REFLECTION

APART FROM ME YOU CAN DO NOTHING

Verses of the Day

Abide in me, and I in you. As the branch cannot bear fruit by itself, unless it abides in the vine, neither can you, unless you abide in me. I am the vine; you are the branches. Whoever abides in me and I in him, he it is that bears much fruit, for apart from me you can do nothing. If anyone does not abide in me he is thrown away like a branch and withers; and the branches are gathered, thrown into the fire, and burned. If you abide in me, and my words abide in you, ask whatever you wish, and it will be done for you. By this my Father is glorified, that you bear much fruit and so prove to be my disciples. As the Father has loved me, so have I loved you. Abide in my love. If you keep my commandments, you will abide in my love, just as I have kept my Father's commandments and abide in his love. These things I have spoken to you, that my joy may be in you, and that your joy may be full.

– John 15:4-11

God anointed Jesus of Nazareth with the Holy Spirit and with power. He went about doing good and healing all who were oppressed by the devil, for God was with him.

– Acts 10:38

REFLECTION

_____

_____

_____

_____

_____

_____

_____

_____

The Kingdom of God Has Come Near to You

Verse of the Day

After this the Lord appointed seventy-two others and sent them on ahead of him, two by two, into every town and place where he himself was about to go. And he said to them, "The harvest is plentiful, but the laborers are few. Therefore pray earnestly to the Lord of the harvest to send out laborers into his harvest. Go your way; behold, I am sending you out as lambs in the midst of wolves. Carry no moneybag, no knapsack, no sandals, and greet no one on the road. Whatever house you enter, first say, 'Peace be to this house!' And if a son of peace is there, your peace will rest upon him. But if not, it will return to you. And remain in the same house, eating and drinking what they provide, for the laborer deserves his wages. Do not go from house to house. Whenever you enter a town and they receive you, eat what is set before you. Heal the sick in it and say to them, 'The kingdom of God has come near to you.' But whenever you enter a town and they do not receive you, go into its streets and say, 'Even the dust of your town that clings to our feet we wipe off against you. Nevertheless know this, that the kingdom of God has come near.'"

– Luke 10:1-11

Reflection

_____

_____

_____

_____

_____

_____

_____

_____

GREATER WORKS THAN THESE

Verses of the Day

So Jesus said to them, "Truly, truly, I say to you, the Son can do nothing of his own accord, but only what he sees the Father doing. For whatever the Father does, that the Son does likewise. For the Father loves the Son and shows him all that he himself is doing. And greater works than these will he show him, so that you may marvel.

– John 5:19-20

Truly, truly, I say to you, whoever believes in me will also do the works that I do; and greater works than these will he do, because I am going to the Father. Whatever you ask in my name, this I will do, that the Father may be glorified in the Son. If you ask me anything in my name, I will do it.

– John 14:12-14

REFLECTION

_____

_____

_____

_____

_____

_____

_____

_____

_____

_____

_____

USE WHATEVER GIFT YOU HAVE RECEIVED

Verse of the Day

Each one should use whatever gift he has received to serve others, faithfully administering God's grace in its various forms. If anyone speaks, he should do it as one speaking the very words of God. If anyone serves, he should do it with the strength God provides, so that in all things God may be praised through Jesus Christ. To him be the glory and the power for ever and ever. Amen.

– 1 Peter 4:10-11 (NIV)

REFLECTION

_____

_____

_____

_____

_____

_____

_____

_____

_____

_____

_____

_____

_____

AMONG THEM

Verses of the Day

For where two or three are gathered in my name, there am I among them.

– Matthew 18:20

On their release, Peter and John went back to their own people and reported all that the chief priests and elders had said to them. When they heard this, they raised their voices together in prayer to God. "Sovereign Lord," they said, "you made the heaven and the earth and the sea, and everything in them. You spoke by the Holy Spirit through the mouth of your servant, our father David: " 'Why do the nations rage and the peoples plot in vain? The kings of the earth take their stand and the rulers gather together against the Lord and against his Anointed One.' Indeed Herod and Pontius Pilate met together with the Gentiles and the people of Israel in this city to conspire against your holy servant Jesus, whom you anointed. They did what your power and will had decided beforehand should happen. Now, Lord, consider their threats and enable your servants to speak your word with great boldness. Stretch out your hand to heal and perform miraculous signs and wonders through the name of your holy servant Jesus." After they prayed, the place where they were meeting was shaken. And they were all filled with the Holy Spirit and spoke the word of God boldly.

– Acts 4:23-31 (NIV)

REFLECTION

_____

_____

_____

_____

_____

_____

_____

THEY DEVOTED THEMSELVES

Verse of the Day

And they devoted themselves to the apostles' teaching and the fellowship, to the breaking of bread and the prayers. And awe came upon every soul, and many wonders and signs were being done through the apostles. And all who believed were together and had all things in common. And they were selling their possessions and belongings and distributing the proceeds to all, as any had need. And day by day, attending the temple together and breaking bread in their homes, they received their food with glad and generous hearts, praising God and having favor with all the people. And the Lord added to their number day by day those who were being saved.

– Acts 2:42-47

REFLECTION

_____

_____

_____

_____

_____

_____

_____

_____

_____

_____

_____

_____

_____

In Remembrance of Me

Verses of the Day

For I received from the Lord what I also delivered to you, that the Lord Jesus on the night when he was betrayed took bread, and when he had given thanks, he broke it, and said, "This is my body, which is for you. Do this in remembrance of me." In the same way also he took the cup, after supper, saying, "This cup is the new covenant in my blood. Do this, as often as you drink it, in remembrance of me." For as often as you eat this bread and drink the cup, you proclaim the Lord's death until he comes.

– 1 Corinthians 11:23-26

Now as they were eating, Jesus took bread, and after blessing it broke it and gave it to the disciples, and said, "Take, eat; this is my body." And he took a cup, and when he had given thanks he gave it to them, saying, "Drink of it, all of you, for this is my blood of the covenant, which is poured out for many for the forgiveness of sins. I tell you I will not drink again of this fruit of the vine until that day when I drink it new with you in my Father's kingdom.

– Matthew 26:26-29

Reflection

_____

_____

_____

_____

_____

_____

_____

_____

_____

_____

Day 40

WALKING IN FRIENDSHIP WITH GOD

Verses of the Day

Enoch walked faithfully with God; then he was no more, because God took him away.

– Genesis 5:24 (NIV)

By faith Enoch was taken from this life, so that he did not experience death: "He could not be found, because God had taken him away." For before he was taken, he was commended as one who pleased God. And without faith it is impossible to please God, because anyone who comes to him must believe that he exists and that he rewards those who earnestly seek him.

– Hebrews 11:5–6 (NIV)

REFLECTION

_____

_____

_____

_____

_____

_____

_____

_____

_____

_____

_____

_____

OTHER BOOKS BY JAMIE MOORE

Friendship with God: Discover God's Relational Presence and Receive Peace, Identity, and Purpose for Your Life

Friendship with God: Discussion Guide and 40-Day Journal

ABOUT THE AUTHOR

Jamie Moore is an elder and pastor at Mariemont Community Church in Cincinnati, Ohio. He holds degrees in music, worship, and theology from Baylor University, Southwestern Baptist Theological Seminary, and B. H. Carroll Theological Institute. His PhD dissertation was on the theology and ministry of A. W. Tozer. Jamie's passion is to help others grow in deep friendship with the Father, Son, and Holy Spirit.

For over twenty years, Jamie has served local churches in Texas, Tennessee, and Oklahoma, before coming to Ohio. Raised in Texas, Jamie is a huge fan of the Baylor Bears, Dallas Cowboys, Texas Rangers, and Dallas Mavericks. He and his wife, Jess, have two kids, Bailey and Caden, and trained together as a family to become black belts in tae kwon do.

If interested in having Jamie speak at one of your upcoming events, you can submit a speaking request at www.jamiemoore.org.

THE POWER OF YOUR REVIEW

Thank You for Reading My Book!

If *Friendship with God* spoke to you and was a source of encouragement, then would you please consider writing a review of my book?

This is encouraging to me and will help potential readers find out about the book as well!

Thank you for reading and reviewing.

May the Father bless you with His presence, His peace in Jesus, and His power through the Holy Spirit. May you enjoy deep friendship with the triune God, both now and throughout eternity.

Much love to you,

Jamie

Made in the USA
Las Vegas, NV
20 September 2022

55669178R00070